Author: Edward Anderson

Co Author: Teresa Anderson

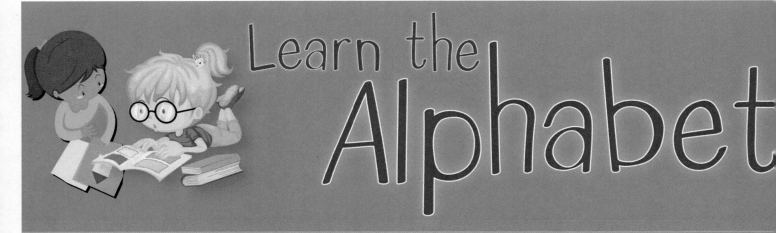

Learn the Alphabet

A is for...

Angel

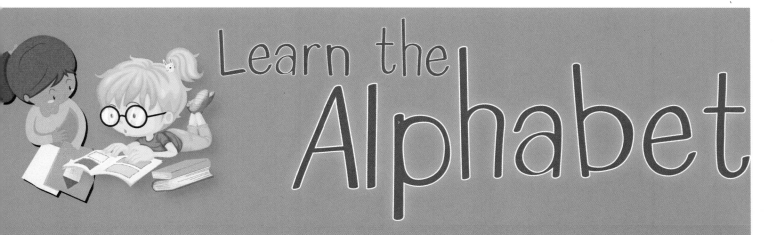

Learn the Alphabet

B is for...

Beautiful

Learn the Alphabet

C is for...

Courageous

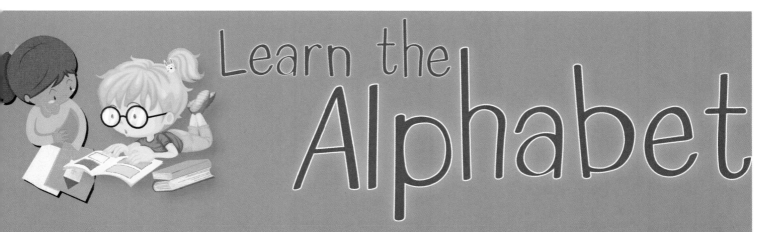

Learn the Alphabet

D is for...

Doll

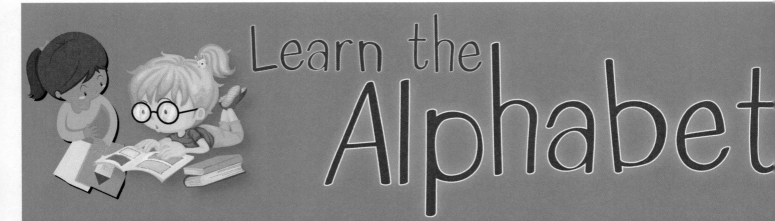

Learn the Alphabet

E is for...

Eager

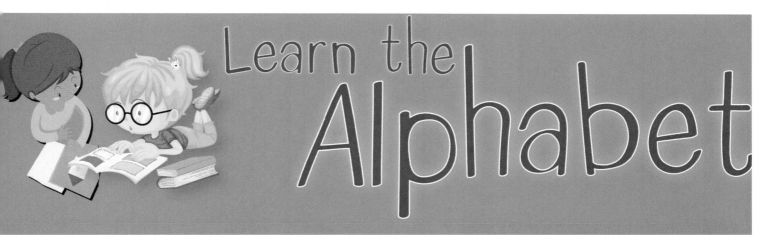

Learn the Alphabet

F is for...

Fabulous

Learn the Alphabet

G is for...

God

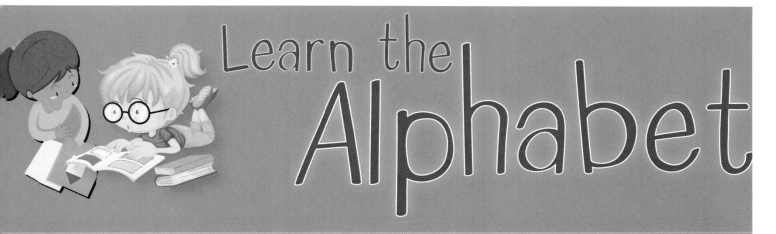

Learn the Alphabet

H is for...

Helpful

Learn the Alphabet

I is for...

Ivory

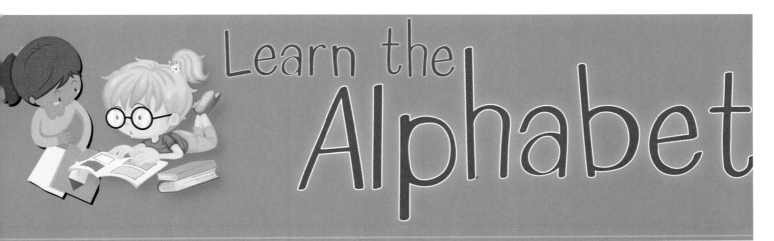

Learn the Alphabet

J is for...

Joy

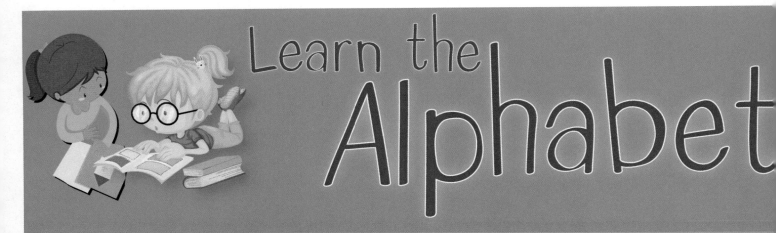

Learn the Alphabet

K is for...

Kind

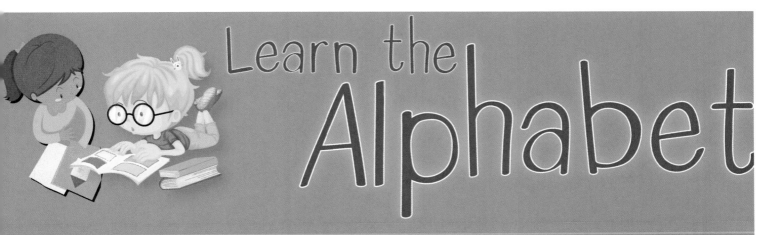

Learn the Alphabet

L is for...

love

Learn the Alphabet

M is for...

Model

Learn the Alphabet

N is for...

Nice

Learn the Alphabet

O is for...

Open

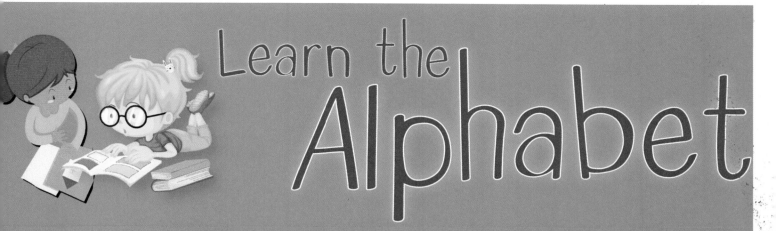

Learn the Alphabet

P is for...

Popular

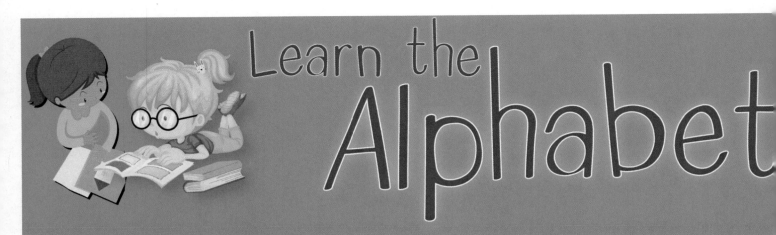

Learn the Alphabet

Q is for...

Queen

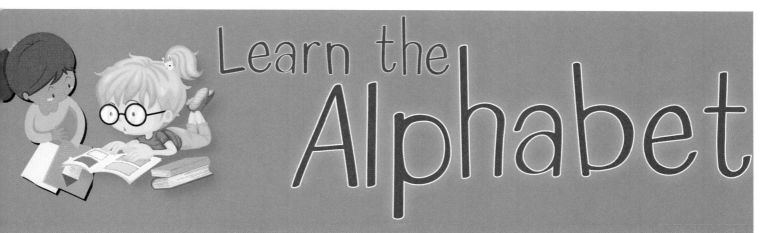

Learn the Alphabet

R is for...

Ring

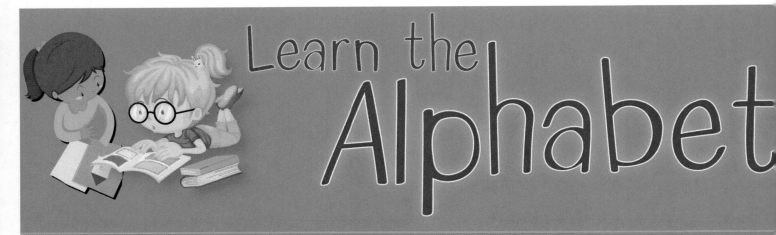

Learn the Alphabet

S is for...

See

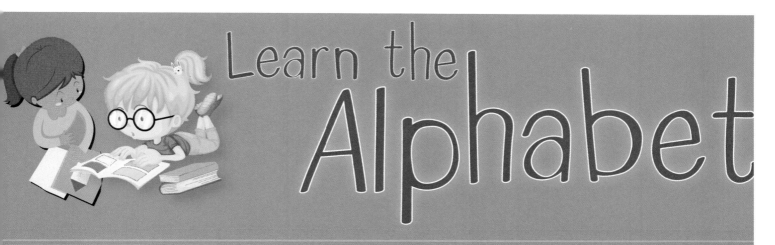

T is for...

True

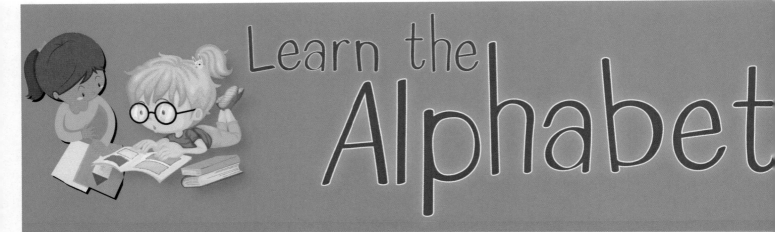

Learn the Alphabet

U is for...

Us

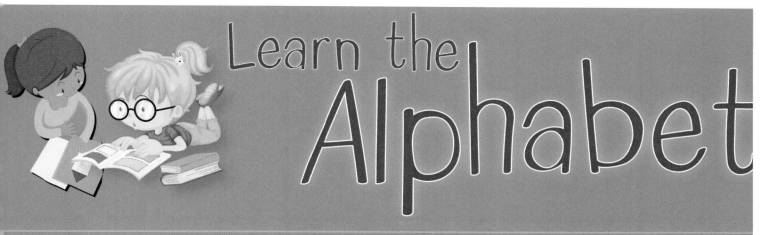

Learn the Alphabet

V is for...

Victory

Learn the Alphabet

W is for...

We

Learn the Alphabet

X is for...

X-ray

Learn the Alphabet

Y is for...

Yellow

Learn the Alphabet

Z is for...

ZOO

Zebra

Made in the USA
Middletown, DE
18 April 2022